Disney's
Princess invites

(your name)

into a magical world, where you can become a princess with Jasmine, Snow White, Cinderella, Ariel, Aurora, Mulan and Belle.

Jasmine

Snow White

Cinderella

Now turn the page to begin the fairy-tale...

Jasmine's Secret Garden

Jasmine takes us on a tour of the beautiful gardens at her palace in Agrabah.

Jasmine sitting by the fountain in her beloved palace gardens.

The Sultan of Agrabah's palace gardens are reputedly the most beautiful in the world. The gardens are thought to stretch for miles and boast a profusion of exotic trees, flowers, shrubs and plants.

To the outside world, the beauty of these gardens has remained a mystery. But, for the first time, the Sultan's daughter, Princess Jasmine, has agreed to show us around the gardens and tell us why

Jasmine walks her pet, Rajah in the gardens.

they have such a special place in her heart.

Princess Jasmine, a vision of beauty herself, greets us and ushers our party into the breathtaking gardens.

As you enter the gardens, your eyes are immediately drawn to a spectacular fountain.

"The fountain is made from the finest white marble," Jasmine informs us. "It was a gift to my great grandfather from a visiting prince."

Jasmine sits down beside the fountain and invites us to join her.

"I often visited this fountain as a child," she smiles fondly. "I would sit by the water's edge, as we are now, and dream of adventures."

In the distance, a tiger emerges through some long grass.

"That's my pet tiger, Rajah," says Jasmine. "He is very friendly."

Jasmine recalls happy memories of playing with Rajah in the gardens, as a young princess.

"Every part of these gardens has a special place in my heart," Jasmine tells us, as we follow her deep into the grounds. Soon we reach a pretty clearing.

"This is a secret glade!" she announces proudly. "Aladdin

Jasmine spends many happy hours away from the responsibilities of being a royal princess.

and I discovered it when we were exploring. This is where we shared a romantic picnic and fell in love."

As we look around the palace gardens, we can't help falling in love with them, too!

Jasmine and Aladdin picnic with Rajah in the palace grounds.

Beautiful Gardens

Jasmine is relaxing in the beautiful palace gardens. How many pink water lilies can you count?

How many lamps can you find in the picture?

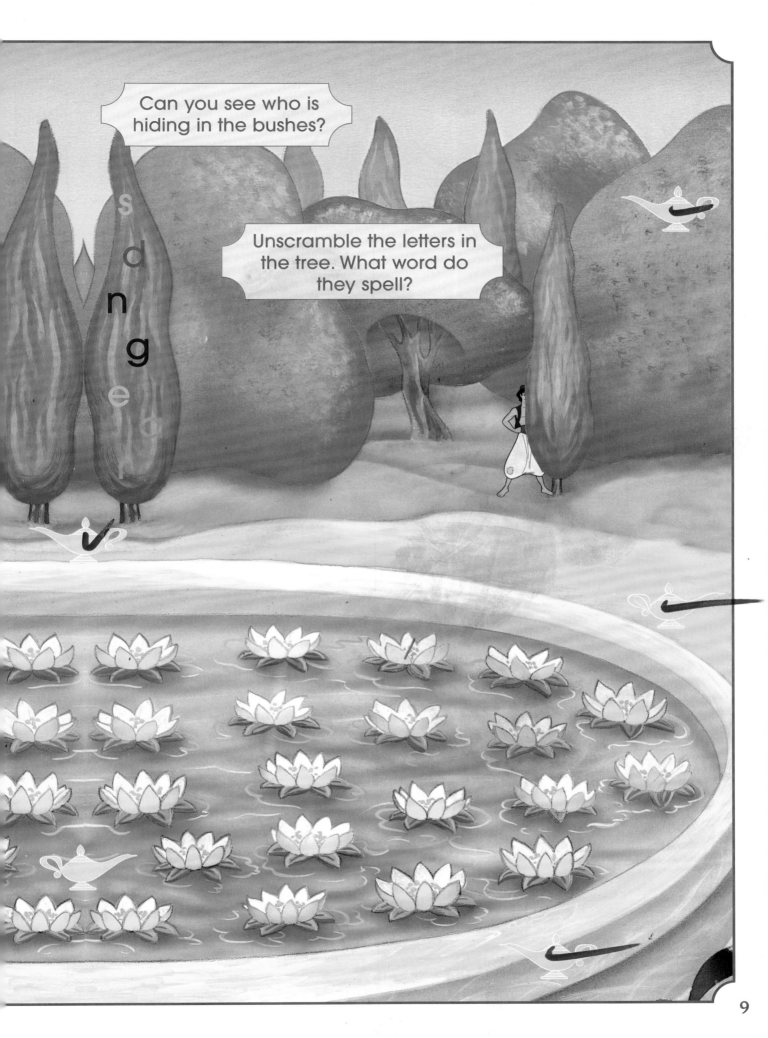

Use the little picture in the turret to help you colour this page.

Jasmine's Flowers

Jasmine loves pretty flowers. Here's how to make some of your own.

You will need:

tissue paper

pliers

glue

green and black paper

scissors

wire

To create the centre of the flower, cut a length of wire and wrap a small strip of black paper around one end.

Princess tip! Make several flowers and arrange them in a pretty vase.

Cut petal shapes out of coloured tissue paper and glue these around the centre of the flower.

To finish the flower, wrap a thin strip of green paper around the wire until you reach the end, to complete the 'stem'.

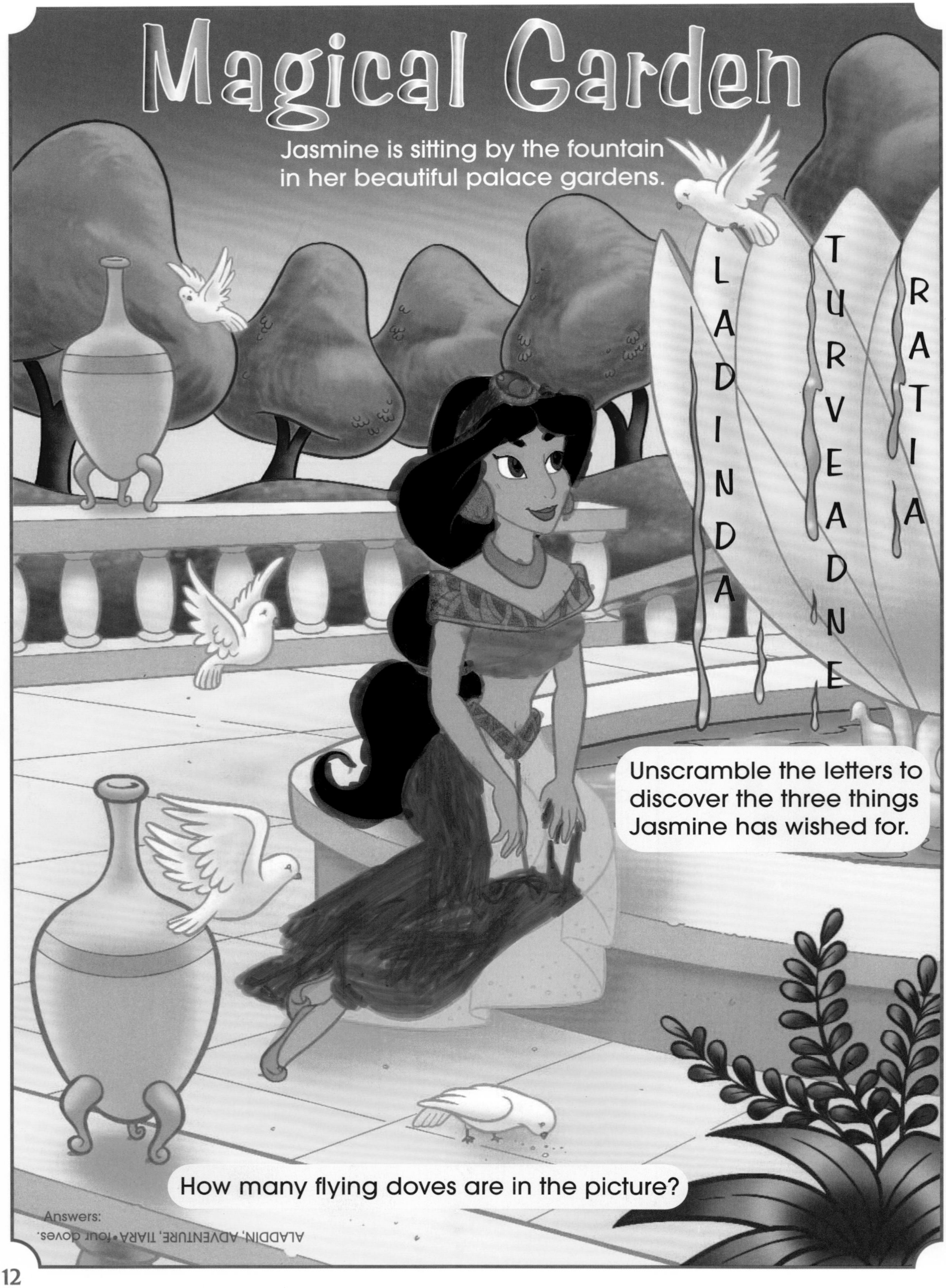
Magical Garden
Jasmine is sitting by the fountain in her beautiful palace gardens.
LADINDA
TURVEADNE
RATIA
Unscramble the letters to discover the three things Jasmine has wished for.
How many flying doves are in the picture?
Answers:
ALADDIN, ADVENTURE, TIARA • four doves.

Jasmine's Garden Tips

- Most importantly, always keep your garden tidy.

- Fill your garden with colourful and fragrant flowers.

- Ask your parent/guardian if you can create your own garden feature, perhaps decorating a flowerbed with shells and pretty flowers.

- Grow your own vegetables and fruit — they will taste delicious.

- Always have a comfortable garden chair in which to relax and admire your garden.

Indoor Garden

If you do not have a garden, you could make yourself this beautiful indoor garden.

1) Fill a biscuit tin with garden compost. Wind a cake trim around the outside.

2) Bury a small mirror in the compost for a pond effect. Then create a path with sand.

3) As a final touch, plant lots of flowers and foliage in your garden.

Snow White

The 1937 classic, Snow White and the Seven Dwarfs makes a long-awaited DVD debut in October 2001.

Snow White enjoying her life at the palace.

It was the princess event we had all been waiting for; the DVD premiere of Disney's **Snow White and the Seven Dwarfs**.

At the end of the screening, the audience, filled with Disney princesses and celebrities, rose to its feet and cheered.

It was a glamorous affair

The evil Queen

and a thoroughly good time was had by all.

Disney's Princess reviews the film: **Snow White and the Seven Dwarfs**.

Starring: Snow White, the Prince, the Seven Dwarfs and the Queen.

The plot:

Snow White is a young and beautiful princess who lives with her vain and wicked stepmother, the

Snow White meeting the dwarfs for the first time.

and doing her chores, a handsome prince overhears her. He falls instantly in love with Snow White.

The jealous Queen orders her huntsman to get rid of Snow White. But the huntsman cannot harm Snow White and urges her to flee into the forest and never return.

Terrified, Snow White runs deep into the forest, where some friendly animals lead her to safety and to the refuge of a tiny cottage.

There, she meets the Seven Dwarfs, who invite Snow White to stay with them.

When the Queen finds out that Snow White is still alive, she is furious, and, while the dwarfs are away from

Queen. The Queen is very jealous of Snow White's beauty and fears that eventually it will surpass her own. Soon, her fears come true when 'The Spirit of the Magic Mirror' tells her that Snow White is the fairest in all the land.

One day, as Snow White is singing

Snow White and the Seven Dwarfs spend many happy hours together.

the cottage, the wicked Queen casts an evil spell on Snow White, so that she will fall into a deep sleep, only to be awakened by love's first kiss.

The dwarfs build a crystal casket for Snow White and watch over her.

Then one day, the Prince comes riding by on his horse. He has been searching everywhere for Snow White.

In true Disney spirit, he sadly leans over to kiss his true love. When their lips touch, Snow White wakes. It all

Snow White teasing Dopey and Grumpy.

ends well, with the Prince and Snow White riding home to his castle, where they live happily ever after.

Fantastic scenes:
One of the best scenes in the film features the evil Queen. It is gloriously frightening when the Queen turns herself into an "old hag". The suspense of the poisoned apple scene is further extended by the cavalry of forest animals and the dwarfs riding to Snow White's rescue.

Soundtrack:
The film is sprinkled throughout with wonderful sing-along songs, including 'Heigh Ho', 'Whistle While You Work' and 'Someday My Prince Will Come'.

Most princessy moment:
The most princessy moment, for us, came at the end of the film, when Prince Charming leans over and wakes Snow White with a kiss. It's particularly touching, knowing how the Prince has searched far and wide for his true love.

The evil Queen in disguise to trick Snow White.

**Snow White and the Prince
embrace for the first time!**

As the film draws to a close, we can guarantee, there will not be a dry eye in the house.

Princess verdict:
In our opinion, the Snow White and

the Seven Dwarfs DVD is the perfect way to experience this classic film. It includes fantastic bonus features, behind the scenes footage, and much, much more, providing the most complete package ever assembled for this animated Disney classic.

Princess rating:

Five out of five princess tiaras.

Excellent! An absolute must for any true princess fan.

**Snow White and the Prince live
happily ever after!**

Party Time Fun!

Snow White and the Seven Dwarfs are having great fun together. Join in the fun by trying to solve these puzzles.

Which of the details below are not in the picture?

a   b   c   d   e   f

19

Use the heart to help you colour in this romantic
picture of Snow White and the Prince.

Disney's

Princess

Competition Time!

Here's an extra bonus competition for princess fans to enter.

We have ten super videos of the Snow White and the Seven Dwarfs film, to be won in this simple to enter competition.

Walt Disney's film is filled with adventure, real magic and humour.

How to enter

All you have to do is unscramble these letters to spell out the names of three of the Seven Dwarfs.

1) u f l h a s b   2) p l y e s e   3) y o p d e

Write your answers on a postcard or the back of a sealed envelope (don't forget to put your name, address and age) and post to:-

Egmont Books Limited
Unit 7, Riverside Park
Bollin Walk
Wilmslow
Cheshire
SK9 1BJ

Rules
1) 10 winners will be chosen at random and notified by post.
2) Judges' decision is final. No correspondence will be entered into.
3) The winners' names will be made available from Egmont Books Ltd, (on request) after February 8, 2002. Please enclose a stamped addressed envelope for reply.
4) Employees (and their relatives) of Egmont Books Limited and their associated companies are not eligible to enter.
5) Entries are limited to one per person.
6) Competition is open to residents of the UK, Channel Islands and Ireland only.
7) The Publishers reserve the right to vary prizes, subject to availability.
8) Closing date for entries is February 1, 2002.

Cinderella's Diary

Cinderella has recorded one week of her exciting princess lifestyle in a diary, just for us.

Monday

As always, I wake to the sound of my little bird friends singing! Today, I spend my time writing letters and organising my wardrobe.

Tuesday

I spend most of the day shopping for dresses – I love shopping! I have so many balls and parties to attend and I must always look my best!

Wednesday

I visit my favourite dressmaker for a fitting for a new ballgown. I enjoy sketching ideas for dresses, so he can turn them into lovely gowns!

Thursday

In the afternoon, I go to a garden party at my friend's house. Today, I wear a new deep pink dress with matching accessories and gloves.

Friday

My first special event of the week. Prince Charming and I attend a very exclusive ball organised by my friends. I wear my favourite blue ballgown.

Saturday

This evening, I play the piano at a masquerade ball – it is very funny because no one guesses it is me – what fun! I wear a red and white dress with matching mask.

Sunday

Today, I am a judge in the best pet competition at the annual charity gala. I present the prize, which is a beautiful tiara. As you can see, it is great fun being a princess!

Rooms with a View!

Cinderella is visiting her stepmother, Lady Tremaine. Take a look at each room and answer the following questions.

How many rooms have a bed?

Where is Lucifer hiding?

How many rooms are there mice in?

Which two paintings match?

Answers:

Four rooms have a bed•Lucifer is under Lady Tremaine's bed•four rooms have mice•the donkey paintings match.

Fabulous Fan

Add that princess touch with this pretty Cinderella fan.

Cut out a large piece of shiny paper. Glue sections of paper doily along the top edge. Decorate with stickers.

1

Princess tip!
You can decorate your fan with beads, coloured paper, or whatever you wish.

2

Now pleat the paper along the long edge. Start at one side and fold the paper backwards and forwards, like a concertina.

Bunch the pleats together, then open into a fan shape. Staple the bottom and decorate with a ribbon.

3

Charming Changes

Cinderella and Prince Charming are enjoying a dance at the ball. Take a careful look at the two pictures below - can you spot the six differences?

Answers:

Cinderella: bangle missing • headband missing • choker missing • Prince: stripe on side of trousers missing • one epaulette missing • plant missing.

Use the frame to help you colour in this picture
of Cinderella on her terrace.

Princess Preparations

Cinderella's friends are helping her get ready for a party. The blue bird is holding three ribbons. Which one is the shortest?

Jaq has found three beads. How many more can you find?

Can you find the mouse that is wearing a red hat, a blue top, and shoes that don't match?

Think Pink!

Pink really is the colour this season for any self-respecting princess! Take a look at these pictures to see how each princess uses pink in her wardrobe.

Flora stands out in a bright pink dress with matching hat.

Belle brightens up a winter's day with a pale pink skating outfit.

Aurora looks sensational in a bright pink ballgown.

Belle looks lovely in a formal off the shoulder summer dress.

Mulan uses shades of pink to create a very elegant effect.

Cinderella looks as pretty as a picture in this cute deep pink dress.

Princess tip!
You could theme your wardrobe by grouping clothes into colours.

Cinderella looks stunning in this jewel encrusted ballgown, with matching fan.

Princess Paris

The highlight of this year's social calendar was the first Princess Ball, in Disneyland Paris. We sent our royal reporter to cover this glittering occasion.

The winners of the princess competition gather at Disneyland Paris.

I was lucky enough to accompany the European competition winners on a magical weekend where our dreams of becoming fairy-tale princesses would, at last, come true.

On arrival in Paris, we were escorted to a special reception area where we were presented with a 'welcome pack' listing the royal itinerary for the weekend. The itinerary invited us to attend 'Princess Pampering and Preparation' sessions, which would add the

A 'princess' has her make-up applied.

finishing touches to our hair and make-up and teach us to dance with elegance and grace.

But, without a doubt, the highlight of the weekend was going to be the regal ball itself, where we were invited to take part in an evening of fun and finery with Cinderella, Aurora, Snow White and Belle.

The evening of the ball soon arrived. We all felt like true princesses, as we were led to the 'Chalet des Marionnettes' restaurant, dressed in our stunning ballgowns.

Ball

Two lucky 'princesses' share the dance floor with Prince Charming!

Inside the restaurant, we were handed a 'royal cocktail' and amused and entertained by court jesters and magicians.

After enjoying a magnificent buffet, the Court Herald announced the opening of the ball and invited us to follow him to the 'Grand Ballroom'.

A royal fanfare greeted our arrival at the ball. We were then individually introduced to each of the Disney princesses and their handsome princes. Shortly afterwards, a grand orchestra began to play and the princes invited us to join them on the dance floor, for the first dance. As they spun us around the dance floor, we were able to put the steps we had learnt earlier that day into practice.

All too soon, the clock struck midnight and, in time honoured fashion, Cinderella made her hasty exit from the ball. Escorted by 12 princes and the court jesters, we excitedly followed Cinderella to where she was waiting for us in her carriage. We then followed the beautifully illuminated 'pumpkin carriage' through the streets and to the heart of Disneyland Paris.

On reaching the Town Square, a shower of pink and silver confetti fell from the sky, adding that final touch of Disney magic to an already enchanting 'Princess Ball'.

Cinderella leaves the ball in her spectacular coach.

Look out for future competitions in Disney's Princess magazine!

Ariel's Sisters

In an exclusive princess interview, Ariel's six beautiful sisters agree to meet us in a secret location to introduce themselves.

Ariel's sisters are playing in the clear blue water of a secluded bay, as they tell us all about themselves.

Princess Alana

"Hello! My name is Alana. I have brown hair and blue eyes. I have a pink tail and wear a lilac bikini-shell top. I like collecting seashells and swimming."

Princess Aquata

"Hi! My name is Aquata. I have jet black hair that I dress with yellow

Ariel and her sisters love to go shopping together.

sea pearls. I have a yellow tail and wear a yellow bikini-shell top. I like seahorse riding and deep sea diving."

Princess Attina

"My name is Attina and I am the oldest sister. I am brunette and wear a star-shaped tiara in my hair. I have a pink tail and wear a pink bikini-shell top. I like hunting for pearls and sea-flower arranging."

Princess Andrina

"My name is Andrina.

I have blonde hair that I decorate with a fan hairpiece. I have a lilac tail and wear a purple bikini-shell top. I love all sea creatures and swimming."

Princess Arista

"Hello. My name is Arista. I have blonde hair that I wear in a loose ponytail. I have a bright pink tail and wear a bright pink bikini-shell top. I love riding waves and collecting seashells."

Princess Adella

"My name's Adella. I am a brunette and wear blue sea pearls in my hair. I have a blue tail and wear a blue bikini-shell top. I love singing and dancing."

Ariel and all her sisters have a close relationship with their father.

As the interview draws to a close, we watch as, one by one, their tails sink beneath the surface of the ocean into their magical world beneath.

Ariel and her sisters put on a fashion show.

Which of Ariel's sisters has blue sea beads in her hair?

Unscramble the letters in the bubbles to find two secret words.

Answers:
Sebastian is on the arm of the throne • sister f has blue beads in her hair • mermaids and princess • sister b has the longest scarf.

At Home with Aurora

Princess Aurora shows us around the beautiful castle she calls home, which she shares with Prince Phillip.

Aurora looks across the formal gardens within the castle walls.

As we travel deep into the countryside, Aurora's fairy-tale castle appears romantically on the horizon. When you view it for the first time it is a truly breathtaking sight. Its turrets soar up into the sky and its golden spires sparkle in the sunlight.

As our carriage clatters across the creaking drawbridge and through the castle

Aurora and Prince Phillip at the castle gate.

gates, we really feel we are becoming part of a fairy-tale. A trumpet fanfare announces our arrival as Princess Aurora and Prince Phillip cross the courtyard to greet us. "Welcome to our home," Aurora smiles, looking a vision of beauty in a stunning blue gown. "You must be in need of refreshment," Prince Phillip adds, in welcome.

We follow the royal couple inside to an elaborate dining room, where a splendid feast has been prepared. Seated around a large oak table are Aurora's fairy friends, Merryweather, Flora and Fauna.

Afterwards, we are taken on a grand tour of the castle, down the many corridors and winding staircases, through huge state rooms, to the chamber where 'Sleeping Beauty' is said to have slept for a hundred years and finally to the throne room itself.

When we enter, courtiers and ladies in waiting buzz around Princess Aurora and Prince Phillip and see to their every need. They make us feel incredibly welcome, too.

Aurora is a great cook and loves spending time in the kitchen.

So welcome, in fact, that we don't want this amazing fairy-tale to ever end!

Aurora and Prince Phillip love to share their home with friends.

Sleeping Beauty

Use the picture in the banner to help you colour in the moment when Prince Phillip wakes Aurora with a kiss.

Castle Capers

Who's going to reach Princess Aurora first – Prince Phillip or Maleficent? Play this game to find out. All you need is a dice.

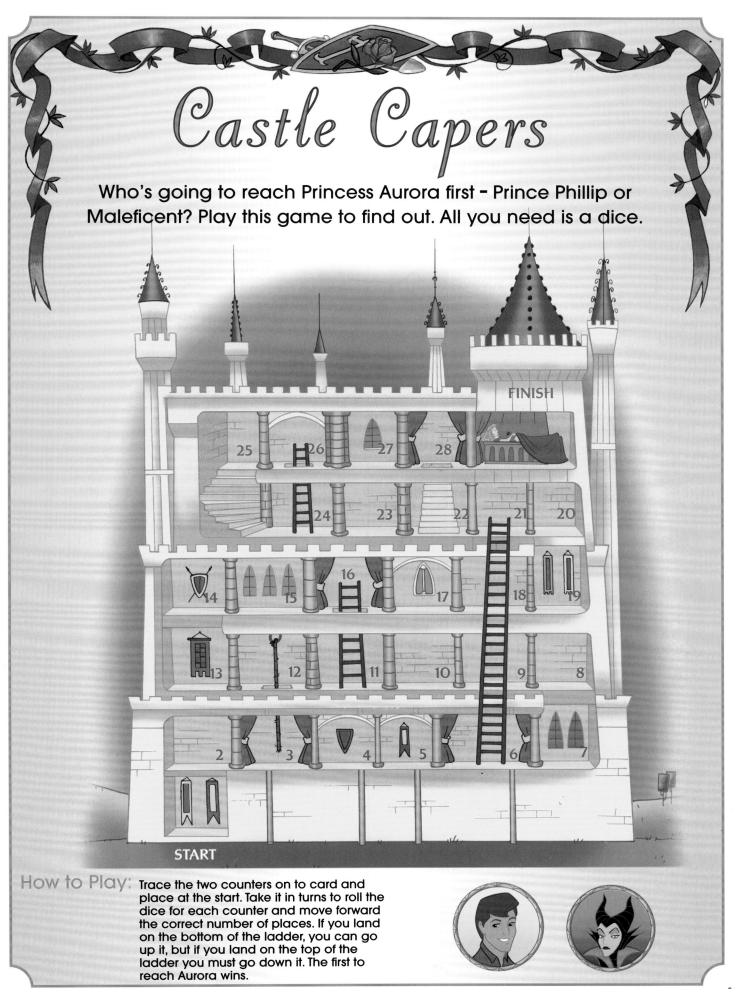

How to Play: Trace the two counters on to card and place at the start. Take it in turns to roll the dice for each counter and move forward the correct number of places. If you land on the bottom of the ladder, you can go up it, but if you land on the top of the ladder you must go down it. The first to reach Aurora wins.

Mulan's Own Story

For the first time, in an open letter Mulan tells her story of meeting the Matchmaker.

Dear Reader

My name is Fa Mulan and I am a princess in China. I live with my parents Fa Zhou and Fa Li. In my country it is the duty of a daughter to bring honour to her family. One way of doing this is to make a good match in marriage. The person who arranges marriages in China is called the Matchmaker.

Let me tell you about the time it was my turn to meet the Matchmaker.

On the day, I was very reluctant and it took a lot of persuasion from my mother to get me ready in time.

My hair was washed, combed and styled into a beautiful bun on the top of my head. Traditional white make-up was applied to my face and I was dressed in elegant silk clothes. But, although I looked

beautiful, I didn't feel myself. As I left to meet the Matchmaker, Grandma Fa gave me a little cricket, called Cri-Kee, for good luck.

However, my meeting with the Matchmaker was a disaster. I was very nervous and my new friend Cri-Kee escaped from his cage and jumped into the Matchmaker's cup of tea. This made the Matchmaker leap into the air, setting her clothes alight on a stove behind her! She was furious and sent

me home in utter disgrace.

I was so ashamed that I hid in our garden. My father found me and tried to comfort me. He pointed to a bud of blossom in a tree and said that, although the bud may be late to bloom, when it eventually does it will be the most beautiful of all. He made me realise that one day I will bloom, too, and bring honour to my family. I am very lucky to have such a wise father.

With love
Mulan
xx

Matchmaker Fun!

Mulan is preparing to meet the Matchmaker. On her way there she found these puzzles for you.

What do the numbers on Mulan's parasol add up to?

Which two parasols have the same patterns?

Princess Necklace

Charm all your friends with this fabulous princess necklace.

1

Ask an adult to help you cut a piece of jewellery wire, enough to hang loosely around your neck.

2

Cut some circles out of the coloured card. Fold into cone shapes and glue into position.

3

Cut up some pieces of coloured straws. Then thread cones, straw pieces and beads on to wire.

You will need:

glue

card

straws

jewellery wire

beads

pliers

scissors

Princess tip!
Twist the two ends together to fasten.

Make Mulan's party go with a bang! Colour in the fireworks, then add some glitter for extra sparkle!

Belle and the Beast

It was happy ever after for Belle and the Beast.
Belle tells us about the time they first met and
when she realised it was true love.

**Belle and the Beast on the balcony of
their castle on a beautiful evening.**

Beauty and the Beast is a well-known love story about a wicked enchantress who put a spell on a handsome but selfish prince so he would remain a beast until he learned to love and was loved in return.

For the first time ever, Belle tells us the truth

**The Beast even brought Belle
breakfast in bed!**

about their remarkable love affair.

How did you first meet?

"One day, my father left home on a trip. On his way through the forest he was chased by wolves and his horse ran off. Fearing for his life, my father sought shelter in the Beast's castle. But the Beast found him and threw him into a dungeon. When

I discovered what had happened, I promised to stay with the Beast in exchange for my father's freedom.
At first, I was afraid of the Beast, but then we slowly became good friends."

When did you first realise you were in love with the Beast?

"It was after the Beast had released me from the castle to go and visit my sick father. My father had told the villagers all about the Beast and they decided they wanted to hunt him down. So I

The Beast was always giving Belle flowers and presents.

went to the Beast's castle and ran to his side, just as Gaston stabbed him in the back. The Beast fell to the ground, wounded. As I held the Beast in my arms, I choked back tears and told him that I loved him. Then, the most magical thing happened. The Beast turned back into a handsome prince, right before my very eyes. I remember it as if it were yesterday; how we couldn't stop looking at each other, how our eyes and hearts were filled with wonder and love - the love that broke the enchantress's spell and brought us happiness forever."

Belle and her prince lived happily ever after!

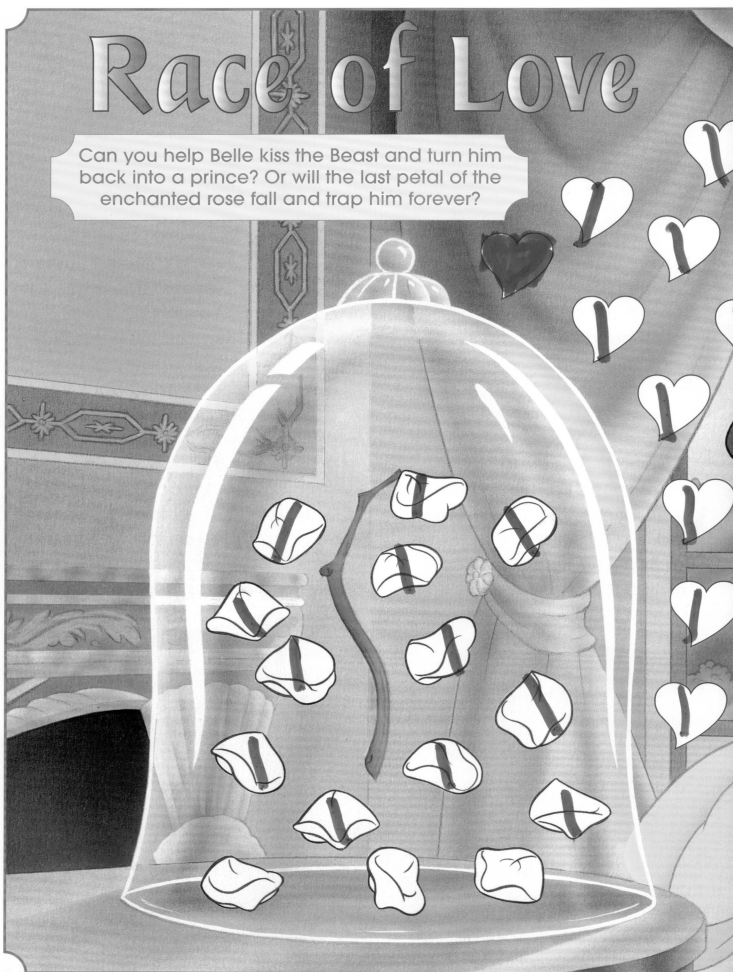

Race of Love

Can you help Belle kiss the Beast and turn him back into a prince? Or will the last petal of the enchanted rose fall and trap him forever?

You will need a dice and a coloured pencil to play. Roll the dice. If it is an even number, colour in one of the hearts. If it is an odd number colour in one of the petals. If the hearts are coloured in first the Beast is saved, but if the petals are finished first, the spell remains unbroken.

Copy the little picture in the mirror to
help you colour in Belle and the Beast.

Beautiful Balcony

If you take the yellow roses away from the pink roses in the bush, how many are left?

How many blue birds are sitting on the Beast and how many pink birds?

Who is hiding in the picture?

Answers:
Two roses • ten blue birds, eight pink birds • Lumiere.

53

Princess

*Try these princess recipes – they will add
the perfect touch to any event!*

Princess Sundaes

Ingredients

Lemonade, ice-cream, strawberry
cordial, 'hundreds and thousands',
sugar, food colouring.

1) Mix a few drops of colouring into
some sugar. Dip the rim of a glass into
water, then into the coloured sugar.
2) Put two scoops of ice-cream into the
glass. Pour cordial over the top.
3) Fill the glass with lemonade, then
sprinkle with 'hundreds and thousands'.

Sugar Mice

Ingredients

Silver balls, sweet laces, white chocolate buttons,
100ml condensed milk, 150g icing sugar, 75g
desiccated coconut, red food colouring.

1) Mix icing sugar, coconut and condensed
milk into a stiff paste. Split into two bowls.
2) Add a few drops of food colouring to
one bowl.
3) Shape the mixtures into mouse
shapes and make eyes, ears and tails
from the silver balls, white chocolate
buttons and sweet laces.

Recipes

Princess Palace

Ingredients

Wafer, jam, cake mixture, sweets, icing sugar, cocktail sticks, ice-cream cones.

1) Make two square cakes. Cut one into four squares and place a square on each corner of the other cake.

2) Place an ice-cream cone on each corner and secure with jam.

3) Cover the whole cake with white icing.

4) Decorate the cake with assorted sweets. Add a wafer for the palace door.

Christmas Logs

Ingredients

Chocolate logs, icing sugar, tubes of red and green icing, candles.

1) Lightly dust each log with icing sugar.

2) Place a candle in the middle of each log.

3) Use coloured icing to decorate the logs with 'holly' leaves and berries.

Princess

It's that time of year again – The Princess Awards. See if you agree with the results.

Most Adventurous Princess
Jasmine

olivia (handwritten)

Best Dancer
Mulan

Georgia Lloyd ✓ olivia (handwritten)

Best Dressed Princess
Belle

olivia G (handwritten)

Put a photograph of yourself here.

Awards

Most Kind to Animals
Snow White

Best Party Organiser
Cinderella

Most Sporty Princess
Ariel

Princess
nivia.
Your name
Best.....kit....
Princess

Princess

Find out which princess you share a star sign with, and discover how similar you are!

Aquarius

21 January - 18 February

Like Pocahontas you are a free spirit. You are friendly, caring, adventurous and a natural leader.

Pisces

19 February - 20 March

Just like Ariel, you are sensitive and a romantic. You love to daydream and your curiosity often gets you into trouble!

Gemini

22 May - 21 June

You have lots of friends, just like Cinderella. You are practical, kind, caring and very romantic.

Cancer

22 June - 22 July

Like Aurora, you are home loving and enjoy having friends over. You are caring, kind, practical and a great cook!

Libra

23 September - 23 October

Just like Jasmine, you are very friendly, loyal and full of adventure. You are passionate, highly spirited and love to travel.

Scorpio

24 October - 22 November

You are loyal, brave and have a curious mind. You love to solve puzzles and enjoy giving tea parties.

Star Signs

Aries
21 March - 20 April

You are fiery and love to lead. Like Esmeralda, you love your freedom and are energetic and kind.

Taurus
21 April - 21 May

Like Melody, you can be stubborn, but also sensible. You are patient, sensitive, kind and very loyal.

Leo
23 July - 23 August

You are very generous and warm-hearted, just like Snow White. You are a great organiser and love to look after other people and animals.

Virgo
24 August - 22 September

Just like Jane, you are practical and well organised. You are a great friend and a perfectionist.

Sagittarius
23 November - 22 December

Like Mulan, you are brave and sometimes take risks. You are cheerful, optimistic and a home lover.

Capricorn
23 December - 20 January

You are very organised, like Belle. You are caring and loyal and love looking after friends and family.

WIN A FANTASTIC FAMILY BREAK TO

Disneyland
PARIS

Visitors young and old can discover the magic of Disneyland® Paris with its Theme Park, its seven themed hotels and of course Disney® Village, the entertainment centre.

The prize:

Includes two nights bed and breakfast for a family of four in a family room (two double beds) at one of the fabulous Disneyland Paris themed hotels, plus three days unlimited entry into the Disneyland Park. And what a time to go!

Disneyland® Paris 2002

From January through March 2002, Kids Go Free to the Magic with Disneyland Paris. Celebrate a world-wide carnival of colours and traditions with all our Disney friends on floats, storeys high with the **ImagiNations Parade**. Summer nights last longer with our Magical Summer Evenings. Main Street Electrical Parade presents a fairyland of lights and illuminations. To top it all, there's the Tinker Bell's, Fantasy in the Sky Fireworks, right beside Sleeping Beauty's Castle. In October, come along and enjoy our hair-raising month-long **Hallowe'en Festival** - it's terror-ific. Then, go BOOM! with the **Bonfire Night Spectacular** in November where the skies light up and see our amazing floating bonfire on Lake Disney®. Then, before you know it, you can celebrate the **Christmas Season** Disney-style and have a **Very Merry Disney® Christmas** all wrapped up for you!

Disneyland® Paris. Come and live the magic.
For more information or a free brochure, call: 08705 030303
or visit: www.disneylandparis.com

| To enter, answer this simple Disney question: | **Name Simba's uncle in the Lion King.** | Send your answer, along with your name and address to: Egmont Children's Books Ltd, Unit 7, Millbank House, Riverside Park, Bollin Walk, Wilmslow, Cheshire, SK9 1BJ. |

The closing date for entries is the 12th January 2002.

Subscribe now and never miss an issue of

Disney's *Princess* magazine

Egmont Magazines Subscriptions

Please note that, unless stated otherwise, the standard order period is twelve months and that new subscriptions take about four weeks to become effective. Sterling cheques and postal orders should be crossed and made payable to: **EGMONT MAGAZINES LIMITED**.

If you wish to pay by credit card or debit card, please remember to write your card number and expiry date in the spaces provided on the coupon and, if you are paying for someone else's subscription, you should add your own name and address in the separate space provided and send to: **Egmont Magazines Subscriptions, PO Box 315, Sittingbourne, Kent ME9 8DT**. Alternatively, call our credit card hotline on **01795 414 906**

Cancelled subscriptions will be subject to a surcharge of 25% (twenty-five per cent) of the full subscriptions or £5.00 whichever is the higher, plus the cost of any issues despatched. Subscriptions cannot be cancelled after they have run for six months or more. Refunds can only be made to the person who paid for the subscription.

I wish to order a year's subscription (13 issues) to Disney's Princess as follows:

United Kingdom £15.40 ☐   Europe £27.00 ☐   Rest of the World £30.60 ☐

Subscriber:

FULL NAME .... (DP0039)

ADDRESS ....

....

POSTCODE .... TELEPHONE............................

BIRTH DATE ....

Person Making Payment (If different from subscriber above)   Mr ☐   Mrs ☐   Ms ☐

FULL NAME ....

ADDRESS ....

....

POSTCODE .... TELEPHONE............................

I am the Parent/Brother/Sister/Aunt/Uncle/Grandparent/Friend/ ....of the subscriber

I enclose a crossed cheque/postal order for £....... made payable to **EGMONT MAGAZINES LIMITED** UK Bank or Eurocheque only

Please charge £........................ to my VISA/MASTERCARD/EUROCARD

Card Number ☐☐☐☐ ☐☐☐☐ ☐☐☐☐ ☐☐☐☐

Expiry Date ☐☐ ☐☐   Signature ☐☐☐☐

Please tick here ☐ if you do not want to receive notice of special offers or new products.

ORDERS & PAYMENTS TO:- Egmont Magazines Subscriptions, PO Box 315, Sittingbourne, Kent ME9 8DT. Tel: 01795 414 906 Subscription Expiry Date: 15/01/02

Instruction to your Bank or Building Society to pay by Direct Debit

DIRECT Debit

EGMONT

Please use a ball-point pen.

Originator's Identification Number ☐7☐6☐3☐9☐3☐9

Please fill in the whole form and send it to: Egmont Magazines Limited Subscriptions, PO Box 315, Sittingbourne, Kent ME9 8DT

1. Name and full postal address of your bank or Building Society branch

To: The Manager   Bank or Building Society

Address   Postcode

2. **Name(s) of Account Holder(s)**

5. **Reference number** (For Office use only)

3. **Branch Sort Code**
(from the top right hand corner of your cheque)

☐☐ — ☐☐ — ☐☐

6. **Instructions to your Bank or Building Society**
Please pay Egmont **Magazines** Limited Direct Debits from the account detailed on this instruction subject to the safeguards assured by the Direct Debit Guarantee. I understand that this Instruction may remain with Egmont **Magazines** Limited and, if so, details will be passed electronically to my Bank/Building Society.

4. **Bank/Building Society account number**

☐☐☐☐☐☐☐☐

Signature(s) ....

Date ....

Banks and Building Societies may not accept Direct Debit Instructions for some type of accounts.

DPAN001